THE COUNTRY LIFE BOOK OF
CLOCKS

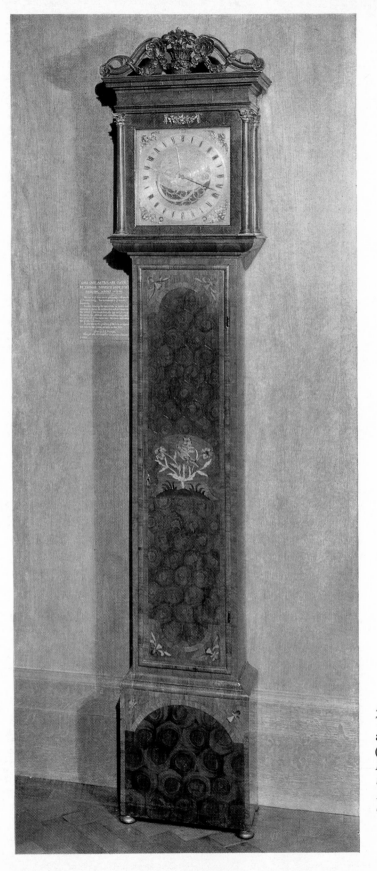

An astronomical clock by
Thomas Tompion made
about 1677.
(*Photograph by Edward
Leigh, by permission of
the Syndics of the
Fitzwilliam Museum,
Cambridge*)

THE COUNTRY LIFE BOOK OF

CLOCKS

Edward T. Joy

LONDON: COUNTRY LIFE LIMITED

First published in 1967
by Country Life Limited
Tower House, Southampton Street, London, WC2
Printed in Great Britain by
Balding and Mansell Limited
Wisbech, Cambs.

Contents

List of Plates

The Georgian Period, 1714–1830

Victorian and After

DIAGRAMS

Introduction

This book surveys the development of English clock-making from its beginning to the present day. Clocks may be regarded in two different ways. Their cases are pieces of domestic furniture which follow the stylistic conventions of their day, reflecting contemporary social conditions and illustrating the craftsmen's varied use of materials and of constructional and decorative techniques. Clock movements, on the other hand, are precision instruments intended to achieve maximum accuracy of timekeeping, and as such they exhibit progress in science and technology. Indeed, in the modern fashion for re-assessing history in technological terms, it may justifiably be held that the increased use of domestic clocks in the 17th century marked the first major impact of science on the home.

It was a happy coincidence that at the time when England was playing a leading part in the development of modern science, her clock-makers produced movements of great accuracy and her craftsmen in wood and metal were reaching the peak of their skill. The result was the 'golden age' of English clock-making, when the craftsmanship of cases and dials worthily matched the intricate mechanism of the movements, and English clocks were in demand all over the world.

The study of antiquarian horology tends to stop abruptly at 1830, a date which is now regarded as arbitrary and artificial. It is true that in Queen Victoria's reign English case-makers lost much of their predecessors' mastery of good design, but the period saw many notable improvements in methods of timekeeping, and many interesting efforts by case designers to restore high standards. It is to examine these, and to assess the achievements and problems of the 20th century, that the story has been continued from 1830 to the present time.

I am greatly indebted to Mr Michael Barnes for his excellent line drawings and his careful study of museum pieces to obtain accurate detail. He received valuable help from Mr P. G. Coole, Senior Conservation Officer, and his assistant, Mr B. Hutchinson, of the Ilbert Collection, British Museum.

My friend, Mr John Stevens, Honorary Secretary of the Antiquarian Horological Society, has given most generously of his time to read the draft text and offer criticism and suggestions, all of which have been gratefully received. I owe to him the reference to Vallin's will of 1603.

Mr Edward Leigh not only supplied many excellent photographs (including those of the clocks in the Fitzwilliam Museum), but also gave much helpful advice.

Acknowledgments

The author wishes to express his gratitude to the following for their generous help with illustrations:

Asprey & Co., Ltd: Plate 83.

Bank of England: Plate 60.

Michael Barnes, Esq.: Figures 1 to 16.

Martin Battersby, Esq.: Plate 84.

G. H. Bell, Esq.: Plate 89.

British Museum: Plates 7, 8.

E. Dent & Co., Ltd: Plates 85, 86, 87, 88.

The Syndics of the Fitzwilliam Museum, Cambridge: Frontispiece, Plates 18, 20, 21, 30, 31, 32, 33, 37, 38, 39, 40, 75, 76, 77, 78.

Messrs Heal's, Tottenham Court Road: Plates 90, 91.

Hotspur, Ltd: Plates 17, 19, 22, 24, 34, 35, 36, 43, 44, 46, 53, 54, 58, 68, 69, 70, 71.

H. W. Keil, Ltd: Plates 23, 48, 57, 67.

Edward Leigh, Esq.: Plates 13, 14, 15, 16, 27, 28, 29, 41, 42, 72, 73.

Frank Partridge & Sons, Ltd: Plate 25.

Phillips of Hitchin, Ltd: Plates 49, 50, 66.

E. L. Rice, Esq.: Plate 52.

George Sneed, Esq.: Plates 90, 91.

Messrs Stonor and Evans: Plate 55.

G. W. Wells, Esq.: Plate 59.

Temple Williams, Ltd: Plate 62.

Victoria and Albert Museum: Plates 1, 2, 3, 4, 5, 6, 9, 10, 11, 12, 45, 47, 63, 64, 65.

Private Collectors: Plates 51, 79, 80.

1. From the Beginnings to 1500

Early Methods of Recording and Measuring Time. In primitive societies, in which agriculture was the main pursuit, dawn and sunset determined the daily limits of human activity. Man worked during daylight and rested during darkness. After dusk little could be done owing to the poor quality of artificial illumination. Even in late medieval England, when towns and industries had developed, the craft guilds forbade their members to work after dark as the feeble lighting could only result in inferior standards of craftsmanship.

Medieval Europe produced the first mechanical clocks, driven by weights, which gave the true hour, either by day or night, as John Smith expressed it in his *Horological Dialogues* in 1675, 'by the circular moving of certain wheels and pinions artificially disposed within the body of the instrument'. The importance of the invention was that it created much greater accuracy of timekeeping through the application of repetitive mechanical motion.

Early civilizations had produced two time-measuring devices, the sundial and water-clock, which were both developed over the centuries in a variety of forms. The sundial was the earliest device of all, for the changes in the length and direction of the shadow cast by a man, a stick or similar object, were the most obvious records of the sun's position in the sky and of the passage of time during the day. The sundial was known in Mesopotamia and Egypt. A very early Egyptian type was a cruciform shadow-clock on which the shadow of the cross-piece marked the time on a horizontal scale. Sundials of varied types, on which the shadow of a gnomon or pointer recorded the time on a marked surface, were used extensively by the Greeks and Romans and were passed on to medieval Europe. They remained, in fact, the universal time-regulators for many centuries, even after the invention or mechanical clocks.

Sundials had the great disadvantage of being useless at night and in cloudy daylight weather, and water-clocks were probably first devised to remedy this. The usual form of Egyptian water-clock (*clepsydra*) was a stone vessel from which the water dripped through a small hole, the hours being registered by the level of water within the bowl, which was of conical shape to promote a uniform flow of water; in later centuries these vessels were in wide use. In some cases the time was measured by the flow of water into a container. Some elaborate and ingeniously contrived water-clocks had toothed wheels and even a form of striking mechanism which clearly anticipated the mechanical clock.

In Anglo-Saxon England, time was also measured by the burning of oil lamps and candles. King Alfred, according to his biographer, Bishop Asser, used six 12-inch candles, each burning for four hours, to mark the complete day, and had each enclosed in a lantern of wood and ox-horn to exclude draughts. At some unspecified date in the Middle Ages the sand- or hour-glass also came into use, the regular flow of sand through the narrow junction between two glass bulbs recording units of time.

Early time-indicators employed a different system of time measurement from that of the present day. The daily division of twenty-four hours was known to astronomers from early times, but in everyday life the normal custom was to divide daylight and darkness into equal numbers of 'temporal' hours (usually twelve) which differed in length both between day and night (except at the equinoxes) and between the seasons of the year. Water-clocks and sundials had been designed from early times to allow for these variations.

Moreover, the length of the solar day is not exactly constant throughout the year as the earth's orbit round the sun is an ellipse and not a circle, and the earth's axis is inclined at an angle of $23\frac{1}{2}°$ to the equator. At first only astronomers were aware of these differences between solar time and 'mean' time, i.e. the regular twenty-four hours of the average day. Solar and mean days coincide only on four occasions during the year (about April 16th, June 14th, September 1st, and December 25th) and they vary most (about sixteen minutes) in November. The difference between them is known as the equation of time, and this was to become of increasing importance, as will be seen, when mechanical clocks developed greater accuracy and regularity, and were adjusted to mean time by the sundial.

The modern system of reckoning each day in twenty-four equal hours came into general use in Europe in the 14th century with the advent of mechanical clocks. The convenient method of counting in a double set of twelve hours, starting from midday and midnight, was almost universally established by about 1400, Italy being a notable exception. Previous to this the 'canonical' hours used in monasteries to regulate their daily routine had wide currency, as was natural when monasteries were important cultural centres and the Church dominated men's lives. It was usual to specify the time of day by reference to canonical hours such as 'matins' and 'vespers', or simply to general terms such as 'daybreak' or 'midnight'. But the change to numerical reckoning had obviously been accepted when the famous *Paston Letters* were written between 1440 and 1486, as this extract from a letter sent by Margaret to John Paston in 1453 clearly shows: 'Sir John Heveningham passed to God on Tuesday past last. . . . . his sickness took him on Tuesday at nine of the clock before noon, and by two afternoon he was dead.'

Caution is necessary about the use of the word 'clock'. In its primary sense it meant a 'bell', and was so used until the 16th century. Until then, the name for any kind of time-measuring instrument was '*horologium*' (the Latin for 'telling the hour'), or its English equivalents, 'orloge', and 'horologe'. This can obviously be a fruitful source of confusion. Thus the reference by Chaucer (*c.*1340–1400), in the *Nun's Priest's Tale* in the *Canterbury Tales*, to 'a clokke or an abbey orlogge', to which a cock's crow is likened, means 'a bell or an abbey clock'. 'Horologe' continued to be used after 'clock' had acquired its present connotation, as can be seen in Shakespeare's line in *Othello* (1604):

'He'll watch the horologe a double set.'

Mechanical Clocks. The early history of mechanical clocks in England is surrounded by a great deal of obscurity. Contemporary references to these clocks, such as a written description, or an entry in church accounts of payment of wages to a clock-keeper, or the record of payment for the making or repair of a clock, are always in general and non-technical language. Even in the case of the few surviving clocks to which there is apparently a contemporary reference, it is not always certain whether it is really the same clock, or has the same mechanism. The issue is still further confused by the custom, already noted, of referring to all time-measuring instruments at that period as '*horologia*', making it particularly difficult to distinguish the mechanical variety.

Evidence appears to show that Italy, the birthplace of the Renaissance and of re-awakened interest in science, had the first public striking-clock, which was set up in the church of San Gottardo, Milan, in 1335. Others appeared in Italy before 1350, using the twenty-four hour as opposed to the 2 × 12 hour system which persisted in that country for several centuries. After about 1350 mechanical clocks gradually spread northwards across Europe.

According to Stow's *Survey of the Cities of London and Westminster* (1598–1603), a clock-tower, 'which striketh every Hour on a great Bell, to be heard into the Hall in Sitting Time in the Courts,' was erected opposite Westminster Hall in 1288, the cost being defrayed by a fine of 800 marks on Randulphus de Hengham, the Lord Chief Justice, who altered a roll so that a poor debtor might pay only 6s. 8d. instead of 13s. 4d. Recent research, however, shows that the clock-tower was finished in 1367, and that the clock was installed about 1370, in which year there is record of the payment of 6d. per day to 'John Nicole, keeper of the great clock of the lord King within the Palace of Westminster'.

England has two of the three oldest surviving mechanical clocks in the world, those of Salisbury Cathedral, to which a date of about 1386 can be given on good evidence, and of Wells Cathedral, probably made about 1392. The great clock at Rouen, which is still in existence, was set up there in 1389. The clocks at Salisbury and Wells are so similar that they may very well have been made by the same maker, possibly a foreign craftsman. The Salisbury clock was in regular use until 1844; it was thoroughly overhauled in 1956 and restored to full working condition, being now exhibited in the north aisle. The clockwork of the Wells clock is in the Science Museum, London, but the cathedral retains an old dial and automata (though both are later than the 14th century). This elaborate astronomical dial is set in an arch inside the Cathedral and measures 6 ft. 4½ ins across. The outer-most ring shows the hours in old English numerals in two series of twelve. A gilded star, acting as a pointer, travels round once every twenty-four hours. The next ring, a later addition, shows the minutes. The innermost ring shows the age and phases of the moon. Above the dial two pairs of knights ride round in mock tournament every hour, while the hours are struck by two striking jacks, one outside, the other inside.

The use of striking jacks is typical of those early mechanical clocks, as is the elaborate dial. The jacks took the place of the human clock-keepers who used to strike the bell when earlier clocks, which

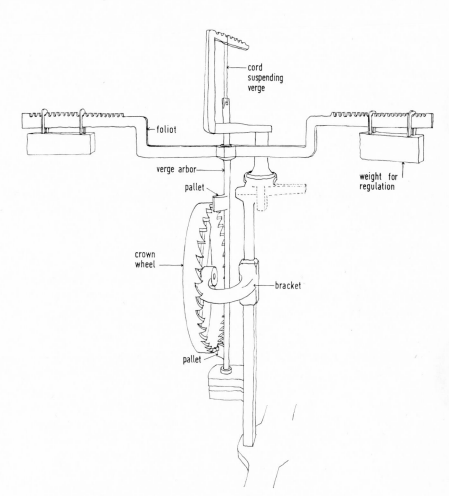

Fig. 1. The verge escapement.

had no dials, set off the alarm. The dial and the striking meant that the clock could tell the time both by day and night, and by eye and ear. These public clocks were conveniently placed in church towers so as to be in a central position, and to have a suitably strong support for their heavy movements mounted in large iron frames. The bells of the tower could be heard far and wide, further than the dial could be seen. The phases of the moon provided essential information for any travellers whose journey might take them until dusk.

From the 15th century onwards clocks were set up first in the cathedral and church towers of the more important English cities and towns, and then in the smaller parishes. It became customary for wealthy citizens to leave money to set up a new clock or maintain an existing one. Few clocks of this period have survived, but three early examples from Dover Castle, Kent, Cassiobury Park, Herts.

and Quickswood, Herts., are still in existence and may have come from the same workshop. They resemble 14th-century clocks in design and workmanship, though they were probably made much later. It is likely that craftsmen from the Continent, where clock-making was more advanced, were employed to design clocks in England, for in 1368 Edward III granted a safe conduct to three Dutch 'orologiers' from Delft to practise their craft in this country for one year.

The making of early mechanical clocks was not a specialist craft, but was the work of the blacksmith, who hammered out the heavy, four-posted open frame and movement—large, coarse-toothed wheels and pinions—in red-hot iron on the anvil. His was skilled work, but it naturally lacked the precision which became essential for accurate working on a small scale.

Weight-driven Clocks. The motive power of turret-clocks was derived from a weight suspended from a rope coiled round a drum. As this weight slowly descended it imparted mechanical motion through a train of geared wheels and pinions. The problem was to achieve regularity of movement as the water-clock had achieved regularity by the steady flow of water through a small orifice.

This regularity was accomplished by a toothed wheel (the 'crown' or 'escape' wheel), set on a horizontal arbor or shaft, the revolving of which was checked by two flag-like pallets fixed at an angle to a vertical arbor (known as the 'verge') (Fig. 1). The pallets engaged and released alternately first one triangular tooth of the crown wheel and then another tooth on the opposite side. The teeth of the crown wheel thrust the pallets first one way then the other, causing the verge to oscillate backwards and forwards and release the train of wheels in the familiar tick-tock movement. Two trains—one for going and one for striking—were necessary.

To control the thrusting force, a heavy bar (or 'foliot'), with two adjustable weights, was fixed at right angles to the top of the verge, so that the crown wheel had to oscillate both verge and foliot. The weights of the foliot could slow down the movement when they were moved to the ends of the bar, and speed it up when they were moved closer to the centre.

It is not known who was the inventor of the verge escapement (the name given to this checking device of verge and crown wheel), or what steps led to its development, but once adopted it was in almost universal use for over three centuries as the controlling agent, until the application of the pendulum to clock mechanism in about 1660, and even after that date it continued in use with some types of clock, notably the bracket (or table) variety (See pp. 34 and 44).

Chamber Clocks. Records of the next major stage in the development of clocks—the adaptation of the weight-driven public clock, suitably reduced in size, for domestic use—are even more scanty than those of early public clocks. There is some evidence that these chamber clocks, as they are called, were known on the Continent in the first half of the 14th century, but the first reliable record of a domestic clock is that of the famous one made in 1364 by the Italian, Giovanni Dondi (1318–89), who ranks among the world's greatest clock-makers. A reproduction of Dondi's clock, made according to the full description which he left, was completed in 1961, and is now in the Smithsonian Institution, Washington, D.C. Its intricate mechanism, however, and its construction in brass instead of iron, put it far ahead of its time. The iron chamber clocks which came gradually into use after 1400 remained expensive rarities. Only very rich people could afford them, even when their production increased in the 16th century.

Late medieval chamber clocks were in almost every way miniature replicas of public clocks. Their weight-driven mechanism was fitted within a rectangular, open, four-posted frame, and they had to be hung on a shelf or bracket projecting from the wall to let their weights hang freely. They usually had two trains, one for going and one for striking. Occasionally a third train (and weight) for an alarm, and a fourth train (and weight) for striking the half-hours or quarters, might be incorporated.

This type of clock had the disadvantage of being a fixture on the wall, and could not be moved from room to room; on the other hand, when it was placed in the hall, the centre of communal life in the castle or manor house, its large bell could be heard striking the hours by all members of the household. Its framework now began to receive attention and was often decorated, like contemporary

1. German chamber clock in frame of gilt brass, movement partly renewed. Early 16th century.
2. German wrought iron chamber clock. Late 16th century.

furniture, with Gothic ornament. The corner posts were shaped like church buttresses, and surmounting the bell (or bells) on top of the clock might be found a spire or pinnacle decorated with crockets (Plates 1 and 2).

These early chamber clocks were made entirely on the Continent, and there is no evidence that English craftsmen played any part in their development. Reference to such clocks in England in the 15th and early 16th centuries are almost certainly to foreign-made, imported examples. Not until after 1550 did a distinctly English type of domestic clock appear.

The backwardness of English clock-making at that time may be explained by the special position which the English blacksmith had long held; for the development of the small chamber clock was the work of a new type of craftsman, the locksmith. Though both the locksmith and blacksmith worked in iron, their techniques were quite different, for while the blacksmith's medium was red-hot iron, on which he had to work at the fastest possible speed ('to strike while the iron is hot'), the locksmith worked in cold iron, with file, saw, vice and drill, bolting or riveting his work, or using the mortice and tenon like a joiner; slow precision, not speed, was his aim. The Continental locksmiths, particularly in Italy, France, Germany and the Netherlands, were far ahead of their English counterparts, and the rise of their craft in the later Middle Ages dealt a sad blow to the English blacksmiths, whose function degenerated gradually into one of merely preparing the iron for the locksmith's use.

The Balance. A new form of regulator, known as a balance (or balance wheel), was developed for use in chamber clocks as an alternative to the foliot, which was not so suitable for small clocks. The balance took the form of a wheel fixed to the head of, and at right angles to, the verge, and it acted in the same manner as the foliot (Fig. 2). Its rate of oscillation, however, was governed by the force

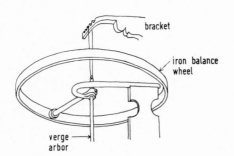

Fig. 2. The balance.

employed (i.e. the weight, or, later, the spring—see p. 17), and it was not so easy to regulate as the foliot, with its adjustable weight at each end. To slow down or speed up the movement of a clock with a balance, it was found best to make the weight lighter or heavier.

The date of development of the balance is unknown, but it may have been invented earlier than has usually been considered, for Dondi used a balance on his clock of 1364; this regulator may well have been used as an alternative to the foliot from quite early times.

2. The Tudor and Early Stuart Periods, 1500-1660

Spring-driven Clocks. The great disadvantage of the weight-driven clock was that it could never be made portable. The search for a more suitable motive force for small clocks led to the introduction of the coiled spring. Its use meant that for the first time clocks could be carried about, and some could be made small enough to be carried on the person, in the form of what would now be termed watches. The credit for making the first true watches is usually given to a German locksmith, Peter Henlein of Nuremberg, between 1500 and 1510, but they are now known to have been made in Italy before the end of the 15th century.

The introduction of the spring posed the question of how to even out its pulling power which was obviously greater when it was fully wound than when it was running down. Such a problem did not arise with the constant motive power exerted by a falling weight.

The earliest device to control the spring's pull was the 'stackfreed', an auxiliary spring which pressed on a cam and provided greater opposition to the fully wound mainspring, and assisted it when it had nearly run down. The word 'stackfreed' is of unknown origin, and was first applied to the device about 1750, long after it had been abandoned by its chief users, the south German makers.

An altogether more efficient device was the fusee, one of the most brilliant inventions in clockmaking. This was a conical drum with a spiral groove, round which a chain, gut or light cord was wound, connected to the outside of the barrel in which the mainspring was housed. When the spring was fully coiled, the chain was at the narrower end of the fusee, where it exerted only a small leverage. When, however, the spring was nearly run down, the chain was at the wider end of the fusee, giving greater leverage and making the pull of the spring constant (Fig. 3 and Plate 16).

The inventor of the fusee is unknown. It was sketched by Leonardo da Vinci about 1485–90, but it seems to have been known about 1450. Its earliest surviving use on a clock has been traced to one made by Jacob Zech in 1525. The device is still used in spring-driven clocks and chronometers.

The earliest portable clocks are sometimes known as drum clocks from their usual flat cylindrical form a few inches in height and about 6 in. in diameter (Plate 3). They were designed to stand on

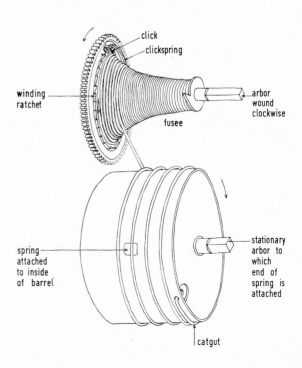

Fig. 3. The fusee and spring barrel.

3. Spring-driven table (drum) clock. French, late 16th century.

4. Leather case for travelling clock. French, mid 16th century.

5. Spring table clock in gilt bronze case. Augsburg, *c.* 1560.

6. Gilt copper table clock, said to have belonged to Queen Elizabeth I. Decorated with strapwork and dated 1581.

7. Spring-driven chamber clock, the case of gilt brass. By Bartholomew Newsam, London. *c.* 1590.
8. Spring-driven chamber clock, the case of gilt brass. By Nicholas Vallin, London. Dated 1575 (the hands later).

tables, and had the dial on top, facing upwards, often protected by a metal cover with holes pierced for the hours to show through.

The mechanism of these portable clocks (apart, of course, from their spring drive) was in every way similar to that of the earlier weight-driven clocks, with a balance usually substituted for a foliot. In spite of their usefulness, and the ingenuity expended on controlling their movements, they were in many respects unreliable timekeepers, and were so expensive, owing especially to the cost of constructing the spring, that they were still great rarities. They were regulated either by winding the spring up tighter on its barrel (to exert more force on the fusee and thus make the clock faster) or by using a hog's bristle as a stop to limit the arc of the balance by acting against its spoke.

Unlike, however, weight-driven clocks with their open, four-posted frames, the spring-driven clocks had their mechanism held between two horizontal metal plates supported on pillars, which allowed trains to overlap. It was customary to enclose the whole clock in a metal case, to preserve the mechanism from dust and mishandling. At first iron was used, but after about 1550 brass, copper or sometimes silver became general; if the latter the case would be finely engraved or chased. Their shapes became more varied, square, hexagonal and octagonal forms being found in addition to

9. Table clock, the case of gilt brass with applied silver medallions. The movement signed by David Ramsay, clock-maker to James I. 1603–10.

the earlier cylindrical design, and they were now known as table clocks. The bell was fitted into the body in the early examples, and the case was perforated opposite it so that the striking could be plainly heard. Later the bell was fitted above the top plate, covered by a pierced dome, and later still at the bottom, the case being then fitted with feet. Some clocks were fitted with leather cases for protection when travelling (Plate 4).

In the second half of the 16th century spring-driven clocks of upright form, with their dial placed vertically, were made in increasing quantities on the Continent, particularly in southern Germany, where Augsburg (Plate 5) and Nuremberg were the predominant centres, but also in Austria, and, to a lesser extent, in France, Italy and the Netherlands. Some very fine German examples with elaborate mechanisms and highly decorated gilt-brass cases have survived. Usually a single hour hand showed the time, but occasionally another hand indicated the quarters, and in some rare examples there was a minute hand. Some clocks were fitted with automata, others with dials showing the days of the month, the signs of the zodiac, the phases and age of the moon, and the course of the planets. From their design, some of the more ornate examples are known as tabernacle clocks. These upright clocks could now stand on any convenient shelf or piece of furniture, their dials could be seen across the room, and they could be carried to any part of the house.

English Clock-making, 1500–1660. The Tudor and early Stuart periods provide us with clear evidence of the earliest manufacture of domestic clocks in England, of the production of the first individual English type of chamber clock, and of the gradual development of specialisation among English makers, exemplified in the incorporation of the London Clock-makers' Company.

The traditional connection between blacksmiths and clock-making died hard in England. The emphasis remained on weight-driven clocks, and though some spring-driven clocks were produced in England in this period, the English locksmith was still far behind his Continental fellow-craftsman in the making of delicate and intricate wheelwork and spring mechanism.

The interest shown by Henry VIII (1509–47) in astronomy and timekeeping, and the growing demand by the English upper classes for more luxuries, encouraged foreign clock-makers to seek employment in England. Many French craftsmen are known to have worked here, and it is to them, no doubt, that we owe the introduction to Englishmen of the Continental locksmith's craft of clock-making. This is probably the reason why English spring clocks tended to be based on French models and not on German, in spite of the pre-eminent position which German clock-makers enjoyed in Europe at that time.

French spring clocks were usually made with a complete case, which fitted over the movement, and with a sunk dial, so that the movement and its attached dial could easily slide down from the case. German clocks, on the other hand, generally had their movements fixed to the case with numerous screws, two detachable side doors being the only means provided to get at the mechanism. Their dismantling, therefore, was a complicated business. The French also preferred a plain rectangular case with finials and a pierced dome, quite different from the elaborate case of architectural character favoured by the Germans.

A well-known upright table clock in the French style, one of the very few English clocks of the 16th century that have survived—it is now in the British Museum—was made about 1590 by Bartholomew Newsam, clock-maker to Queen Elizabeth I. Its spring mechanism is in a fire-gilt metal case and is signed by Newsam, who is also known to have made the horizontal type of table clock (Plate 7).

Both these types of clocks were produced in London at the very end of the 16th century by Nicholas Vallin, a member of a Flemish Protestant family who had probably fled from religious persecution in the Spanish Netherlands (Plate 8). Vallin is an example of the foreign craftsman who was making clocks in England side by side with English clock-makers. Both Newsam and Vallin signed their clocks, but there are a number of surviving unsigned clocks of the time, and it is impossible to say whether they were made by English makers or by foreigners resident in England, or whether they were imported from abroad. An intriguing mystery is Vallin's reference in his will (1603) to 'a clocke made in forme of a lookinge glasse wth an alarum wth case all guilt'.

Only a few English spring-driven table clocks of the first half of the 17th century have survived. Prominent among the makers of the time was David Ramsay, clock-maker to James I and Charles I, but in spite of his long career as a royal craftsman he has left only one positively identifiable clock (and a few watches). His fine clock, now in the Victoria and Albert Museum, has his signature on its movement, but its gilt brass case with applied silver medallions and bell dome, and its engraved scene of James I 'grinding of the pope's nose' (which fixes its date at 1603–10), is undoubtedly French (Plate 9). Ramsay had studied the craft in France, and may well have brought French craftsmen back to England to work with him; and it is clear that he was following the customary procedure among English makers of that time of importing their cases from France when particularly fine clocks or watches were commissioned.

Lantern Clocks. After all the uncertainties about English spring-driven clocks of this period, it is refreshing to examine the first domestic clocks which were of indisputable English make and character, although they lacked many of the refinements of Continental clocks. These typically English clocks were designed to hang on the wall and are today known as lantern clocks, from, it is believed, their resemblance to ships' lanterns of the time (Plates 10, 11, and 12). They began to appear in Elizabeth I's reign and continued to be made until the first quarter of the 18th century, and even later in rural areas. Their manufacture indicates that clocks were no longer the luxury possessions of the rich, but were beginning to find their way into the homes of well-to-do merchants and the like, whose furniture, wrote William Harrison in 1587, 'is growne in maner even to passing delicacie'.

Lantern clocks were weight-driven and were regulated by a balance. They had, almost without

10. Lantern clock in engraved silver case. Signed 'D. Bouquet, Londres'. Mid 17th century.

11. Lantern clock with weights, signed 'Andrew Prime Londini fecit'. Mid 17th century.

12. Lantern clock in silver case. Signed and dated 'Edward Webbe in Church Stoke 1676'.

exception, only one hand, and carried a large bell to be heard throughout the house. They were made entirely of metal, at first of iron, and often with Gothic pillars; later, after a short interval, of brass, with classical columns that connected the horizontal plates at top and bottom. There were fixed plates at the front and back, and hinged doors at each side.

The surmounting bell was suspended from four bands which sprang diagonally from behind the corner finials and met in a central boss. Between these bands, at front and sides, were fretted crestings. The dial had the twelve hours in Roman numerals, and the quarters marked in subdivisions on its inner edge. The weights, which took about thirty hours to descend, were normally rewound every twenty-four hours. To let the weights hang freely, the clocks were attached to the wall by a hook and staple and had two extra 'spurs' at the foot to press into the wall to keep them steady.

In the first half of the 17th century lantern clocks were produced in increasing numbers. They were very much of a standardised pattern, varying only in size and minor details. This suggests that their various components were made by specialist craftsmen, and certainly specialisation became an established feature of English clock-making as the century advanced. The long control of the Blacksmiths' Company over clock-making ended when the Clock-makers' Company was incorporated in London in 1631, after a petition to the Crown. London now became the main centre of the craft, although lantern clocks were also made in provincial towns. The new Company's ordinances showed that clock-makers, mathematical instrument-makers, sundial-makers, gravers and case-makers were all included in the trade. Once protection had been given to the craft, competition with alien craftsmen in London ceased (for the Company controlled both native and alien clock-makers in London), outsiders were rigorously excluded, and specialisation was bound to increase still further.

3. The Late Stuart Period, 1660-1714

The Pendulum. The inclusion of sundial-makers among the specialist craftsmen of the new Clockmakers' Company may, at first sight, appear surprising when so many advances were being made in clock-making. It is a reminder, however, that both weight- and spring-driven clocks were, in spite of all the improvements, poor timekeepers, and that it was still necessary to set them right every day by the sundial. In the first half of the 17th century, therefore, the sundial-maker had an essential function to perform. Even the best clocks could rarely keep closer time than to a quarter of an hour each day.

Shortly after 1650, however, really accurate timekeeping became possible with the introduction of the pendulum as the regulator of the rate of rotation of a clock's wheels. This marks perhaps the greatest event in the history of horology. In earlier clocks, neither the foliot nor the balance had a uniform swing of its own, for each was controlled by the pull of the weight or spring. The pendulum, on the other hand, has a definite period of swing and gives a repeated unit of time. This regularity can be transmitted to the weight- or spring-driven train of wheels which then in effect records the pendulum's swing and at the same time provides the motive power to keep it swinging. As the pendulum's time of swing depends on its length, its adjustment, by raising its bob to shorten it and make it go faster, and lowering the bob to slow it down, is a very simple matter. The pendulum not only opened a new world to clock-makers, it could also be applied to existing clocks using the old foliot and balance regulators, and many were converted to the new pendulum control.

The considerable research that has been made into the origins of the application of the pendulum

13. Pediment bracket clock in ebony by Henry Higginson, *c.* 1662. Converted to anchor escapement.
14. Back plate of clock by Higginson.

to timekeeping indicates that after the famous astronomer, Galileo, had discovered the isochronous property of the pendulum in 1581, his son, Vincenzio, probably made a pendulum clock. But the credit for the first successful construction—in 1657—of such a clock must go to the great Dutch scientist, Christiaan Huygens van Zulichem, who demonstrated beyond all doubt its true importance (Fig. 5). In 1657 Huygens assigned the rights of his invention to Salomon Coster, a clock-maker of The Hague. John Fromanteel, member of a famous London family of clock-makers of Dutch

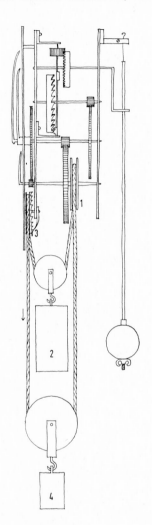

Fig. 4. (*Above*) Huygens's endless rope, which passes over pulley (1) and supports driving weight (2), then goes over ratchet pulley (3) and supports small weight (4). The arrow indicates where the rope is pulled to wind up the driving weight, which continues to drive the clock.

Fig. 5. (*Left*) Huygens's drawing of his timepiece (from his *Horolgium*, 1658) controlled by a pendulum and driven by a weight through an endless rope.

descent, worked with Coster in Holland for a year between 1657 and 1658, and introduced the new principle to England on his return. John was an apprentice of Ahasuerus Fromanteel, who in the *Commonwealth Mercury* in November, 1658, advertises: 'There is lately a way found for making clocks that go exact and keep equaller time than any now made without this regulator. . . and may be made to go a week or a month or a year, with one winding up . . . and is very excellent for all house clocks that go either with springs or weights. . . . Made by Ahasuerus Fromanteel, who made the first that were in England.'

   The movement of a spring pendulum clock, without dial or case, has its backplate engraved *A. Fromanteel London Fecit 1658*, and this must be one of the very first pendulum clocks made in England.

   The fame of the new clocks spread quickly. On May 3rd, 1661, John Evelyn writes in his famous

15. Dial of clock by
Higginson.

16. Split front plate (i.e.
made in two parts for
separate dismantling of
going and striking trains)
and fusee of clock by
Higginson.

17. Bracket clock (formerly at Beningbrough Hall, Yorks.), the case veneered with olive wood oyster
pieces. Spiral turned columns. c. 1675.

18. Ebony long-case clock by Joseph Knibb. Roman striking skeleton dial. *c.* 1680.
19. Long-case clock, the case decorated with floral marquetry. By Thomas Cruttenden, York. *c.* 1685.

20. Movement of clock by Knibb showing locking plate.

diary: ' . . . and I returned by Fromantil's, the famous clockmaker, to see some pendules, Monsieur Zulichem being with us'. ('Zulichem' is Huygens, to whom the diarist refers a month earlier as 'that great mathematician and virtuoso . . . inventor of the pendule clock.')

The introduction of the pendulum clock into England coincided almost exactly with the Restoration of Charles II in 1660. This coincidence proved a most happy one, for after 1660 English clockmaking entered on its 'golden age', and for the next century and a half was to hold a commanding position in Europe. By 1700 English clocks were being exported to all parts of the world. There are several reasons for this remarkable change from comparative backwardness to pre-eminence.

The Restoration of 1660, after the country had undergone eleven years of Puritan republican rule, ushered in what Evelyn described as 'a politer way of living, which passed to luxury and intolerable expense'. During their exile abroad Charles and his court had become accustomed to the more elegant living standards of the Continent, and on their return they inspired a demand for greater comfort and luxury which was eagerly taken up by the whole country, in a reaction against Puritan austerity. There was a notable improvement in the quality of English craftsmanship in which clockmaking naturally shared. The great advances in cabinet-making which occurred in the generation after 1660 were of particular benefit to clock-makers, for the cabinet-maker's techniques of construction and decoration were applied to clock-cases which became an integral part of the furniture of all elegant homes.

The demand for clocks rose considerably after 1660. It received an unexpected stimulus from the

21. Hood of clock by Knibb showing carved cresting and spiral turned columns.

22. Dial of clock by Cruttenden, with fine cherub spandrels.

Great Fire of London in 1666 which led to the rebuilding and refurnishing of a vast number of houses. The demand was sustained by the rapidly growing wealth of the country. By 1700 England was a major commercial and colonial power, and the foundation of the Bank of England in 1694 confirmed her strong financial position.

Of particular importance for clock-making was the greatly increased interest in science at this time, in which England played a leading part. This was the age of Sir Isaac Newton, whose researches are now universally recognised as having laid the basis of modern science. Scientific study received royal patronage and considerable prestige with the incorporation of the Royal Society in 1662. It is no coincidence that Dr Robert Hooke (1635–1703), one of the leading figures in clock-making in post-

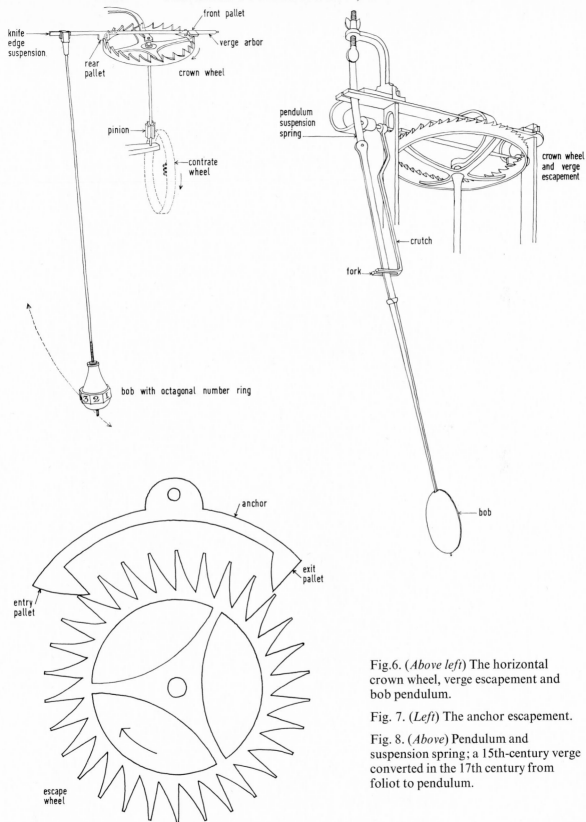

knife edge suspension

rear pallet

front pallet

verge arbor

crown wheel

pinion

contrate wheel

bob with octagonal number ring

pendulum suspension spring

crown wheel and verge escapement

crutch

fork

bob

anchor

exit pallet

entry pallet

escape wheel

Fig. 6. (*Above left*) The horizontal crown wheel, verge escapement and bob pendulum.

Fig. 7. (*Left*) The anchor escapement.

Fig. 8. (*Above*) Pendulum and suspension spring; a 15th-century verge converted in the 17th century from foliot to pendulum.

Restoration England (though some of his claims are now discounted) was a Fellow of the Royal Society, and was led to study horology through his interest in science. 'The new trade of the clock-maker', states Professor G. N. Clark (*Science and Social Welfare in the Age of Newton*, 1937, p. 20), 'owed its existence to science'.

England's special position as a great commercial and maritime power naturally encouraged a widespread study of timekeeping methods (in which Holland, the other leading commercial and maritime power, shared). Greenwich Observatory was founded in 1675 for the practical purpose of 'finding out the longitude for perfect navigation', for which highly accurate timekeeping at sea was essential. Researches by English clock-makers into timekeeping methods for navigational needs were actively encouraged by the government and sustained throughout the Georgian period, the classic age of British sea power, with brilliant results.

At first both weight- and spring-driven clocks used the short ('bob') pendulum, which swung quickly in a wide arc, with the verge escapement. The crown wheel was now placed horizontally, and the pendulum swung the verge, to which it was attached at right angles (Fig. 6). Two major improvements were soon introduced, the long pendulum and the anchor escapement, which, when used in conjunction, resulted in remarkable accuracy. The long pendulum of 39·1 ins (the 'Royal' pendulum) gave a one-second swing in a very small arc. The anchor escapement, so called from its shape, engaged the teeth of the escape wheel, now set vertically again (Fig. 7). The long pendulum was not attached directly to the pallet arbor, as the short pendulum had been in the case of the verge escapement, but hung by a flat spring from the suspension block (Fig. 8). An arm known as a crutch hung from the pallet arbor and was connected to the pendulum, to which it transmitted the impulses from the escapement. Clocks using the seconds pendulum have a seconds dial with a small hand which is fixed to the end of the escape wheel arbor.

The invention of the anchor escapement has for centuries been attributed to Robert Hooke, but it seems to have been first used, about 1670, by William Clement (1638–1704), a leading London clock-maker. The merits of the long pendulum were quickly recognised, for John Smith (*op. cit.*) writes in 1675: 'As to their regularity, I shall say only thus much, that those Clocks, who have their motion regulated by a Pendulum, are more excellent than those who are regulated by a Ballance, and those, that are regulated by a long Pendulum, are far more excellent than those that are regulated by a short one.'

Weight-driven clocks were now made to go for much longer than thirty hours; eight days became common (with weekly winding), but some could go for a month and longer, even as much as a year. Spring clocks were also of eight-day duration, but seldom longer, owing to the awkward size and increased cost of the larger spring that would have been necessary. Spring clocks also persisted with the verge escapement and bob pendulum until about 1815. No doubt this was because they were moved about the house so much that it was difficult to stand them always on a sufficiently level surface to ensure their being 'in beat', the verge escapement being less critical in this respect.

Long-case Clocks. A development probably originating in England was the famous long-case clock, which has become generally known as the 'grandfather' clock ever since it was so named in a popular song of 1878 by H. C. Work. The thirty-hour lantern clocks, now fitted with a pendulum, continued to be made after 1660, and found their way into more and more homes. Wall (or hanging) eight-day clocks with free-hanging weights and a wooden case over the movement (from which they took the name of hooded clocks) were also in use for a time. But the heavier weights required for these eight-day clocks made it more difficult to hang them on the wall. Instead, the tall, wooden, dust-proof case to house the weights and to support the movement and dial, which were covered by a detachable, glass-fronted hood, was introduced about 1660 and was to remain the standard type of domestic clock for over a century. At first the cases were narrow in the trunk as they enclosed only the weights and not the bob pendulum which swung behind the back plate of the movement. They were necessarily widened when, after the invention of the anchor escapement, they also had to make room for the swing of the long pendulum. The wooden cases were the products of specialist clock-case-

23. Long-case clock, the case decorated with floral marquetry. *c.* 1680–5.
24. Long-case clock, the case decorated with 'seaweed' marquetry. *c.* 1690–5.

25. Long-case clock, the case decorated with arabesque marquetry. By Samuel Stokes, Little Britain, London. *c.* 1695.   26. Long-case clock, the case veneered with finely figured walnut. Late 17th century.

27. Bracket clock with double basket top, showing the phases and age of the moon and planetary signs (with names in Spanish). The front draw string causes the hour bell to repeat and the back cord repeats the quarters on six bells. By Charles Gretton. End of 17th century.

28. Front plate of clock by Gretton.   29. Back plate of clock by Gretton.

makers and embodied all the improved technical skills of late Stuart cabinet-making (Fig. 9 and Plates 18, 19, 23, 24, 25, 26, 34, 42, 43 and 46).

The long-case's conspicuous position in the house and its large surface made it an ideal subject for the new decorative processes of veneering, marquetry and japanning. In the first-named method, thin sheets of rare, choice or finely-figured woods, such as ebony (Plate 18), which was very fashionable for a short period after 1660, walnut (Plates 26 and 34), olive wood, kingwood and laburnum, were glued on an oak carcase. Marquetry employed the same technique to build up patterns of flowers (Plates 19 and 23) and other conventional designs with a wide variety of suitably shaped veneers of coloured woods, some of which were stained, scorched or dyed to obtain the required shade. A closely related form known as parquetry consisted entirely of geometrical patterns. In early examples, both marquetry and parquetry were confined to panels, the spaces between being filled with 'oystershell' veneers (i.e. of oval shape, cut transversely from small branches of trees).

Towards the end of the 17th century floral marquetry, which persisted as a decorative fashion longer on clocks than on other pieces of furniture, covered the whole of the front surface, some examples being of outstanding quality (Plate 42). About the same time appeared the English version known as arabesque (or 'seaweed') marquetry which used two contrasting light and dark shades, normally walnut for the ground and box or holly for the intricate patterns (Plates 24 and 25). In the early 18th century many cases were also decorated more simply with attractive walnut veneers (Plates 26, 34 and 43), and it is noteworthy that some of the most distinguished clock-makers of the time preferred this fashion of using the beauty of walnut to achieve elegant lines and fine proportions.

Both veneering and marquetry originated abroad, and it is probable that many of these fine cases were made by foreign craftsmen resident in England, particularly by Huguenots who fled from France to avoid religious persecution after the revocation of the Edict of Nantes in 1685. Almost nothing is known about these case-makers who, like cabinet-makers, very rarely signed or stamped their work. In complete contrast, clock-makers were compelled by Act of Parliament in 1698 to put

30. Miniature bracket clock by Thomas Tompion. Basket top; pull repeat striking on two bells. c. 1700.

31. Construction of the case of the miniature Tompion clock. The moulded base slides forward.

32. Dial of miniature Tompion clock.

33. Front plate of miniature Tompion clock.

34. Long-case clock by Thomas Tompion, the case veneered with walnut. *c*. 1700.

35. Hood of long-case clock by Tompion.

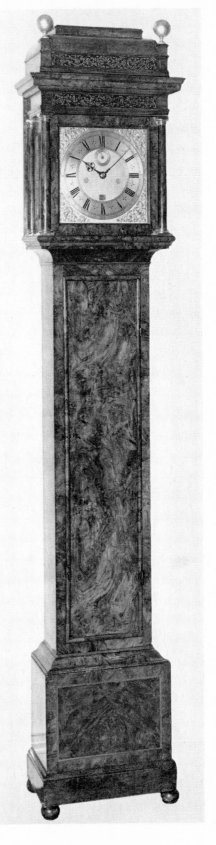

36. Dial of long-case clock by Tompion.

their names and addresses on all their clocks, so that after that date every clock-face carries, in effect, documentary evidence which has helped to accumulate a great deal of information about British makers.

Japanning is the name given to English imitation of lacquer-work, the oriental method of decorating furniture in bright colours of lasting brilliance, which became very popular after 1660 through imports by the East India Company. Only a few 17th-century japanned cases have survived, and probably many which were so treated have been destroyed, owing to the perishable nature of the paint and varnish of japan-work, which is a poor substitute for genuine lacquer. But this mode of ornament became particularly popular for clocks, as will be seen, from about 1710, after English japanners had persuaded Parliament to curtail imports of lacquered furniture by heavy duties.

The earliest long-case clocks exhibited strong architectural influence in the classical style. The hood

hood

glass door
in hood

glass
[or fret]

trunk

trunk door
inset with
vauxhall
mirror

base

W Webster
Exchange Alle
London

break arch

spandrel

seconds
dial

minute
circle

chapter
ring

dial plate

Fig. 9. Long-case clock. Year movement in walnut case, the door panel inset with contemporary Vauxhall mirror glass. By William Webster, *c.* 1720.   Fig. 10. Dial of clock in Fig. 9.

was flanked by columns or pilasters supporting an entablature (architrave, frieze and cornice) surmounted by a triangular pediment. Some columns were spiral-turned, like the members on contemporary furniture, and sometimes a pierced cresting replaced the pediment (Plate 21). Only restricted use was made of carved ornament, which was confined to this pierced cresting—usually arched scrolls centring in a shell, cupid's head or basket of flowers—to the capitals on the flanking columns, to finials, and, more rarely, to the framing round the lantern (or 'bull's eye window') in the trunk through which the swinging pendulum could be observed. Mouldings on the trunk were of ebony, or of wood stained black, or were covered with cross-grained veneer, all of which added greatly to their decorative effect.

When the short bob pendulum was in use, the clock dial was relatively small, about 8 to 9 ins square. This was increased to 10 ins when the Royal pendulum and wider cases were introduced, and to even more—10 to 12 ins—by 1700. The best clocks had gilt brass spandrels, the name for the triangular mounts decorating the corners between the chapter ring and dial plate (Plate 22). The chapter rings were mostly of silvered brass, and the hour numbers, which were engraved in the metal, were filled in with black wax. Unlike lantern clocks, which nearly always had only one hand, pendulum clocks added a long, thin, pointed minute hand, and at first each minute was often numbered on the dial. These dials were always beautifully clear; however many embellishments were added to the clock, the craftsman never forgot its primary function of telling the time (Fig. 10 and Plates 21, 22, 36, 41 and 44).

Just prior to, and during, Queen Anne's reign (1702–14), changes occurred in the treatment of hoods and dials. Some hoods now had a flattened dome on top, above a straight cornice. Tall finials of brass or gilded wood, vase-shaped or spherical, stood at the front corners and on the dome (Plate 42). The pillars flanking the dial glass were straight, and capped and based with brass. The dial was often arched, its line followed by a moulded architrave above, the name broken (or break) arch being given to an arch springing from a diameter less than the width of the case. Clocks were generally increasing in height, sometimes to seven feet and more. One reason for this was that the height of rooms in new houses was also increasing.

Bracket Clocks. Contemporary with the long-case clock was the portable spring-driven pendulum table clock—generally known as the bracket clock—which could be stood on any handy piece of furniture or on a small wall bracket. As already noted, this kind retained the verge escapement and fixed bob pendulum long after the more accurate anchor escapement and spring-suspended pendulum had been introduced into the long-case clock. For a short period after 1660 such clocks had cases of marked architectural character (Plate 13), soon to be superseded by square cases and flattened wooden domes (or 'basket tops') with handles for carrying them about the house (Plate 30). Ebony veneer was a very favourite decoration (Plate 13). Sometimes ebonised pearwood, walnut, kingwood or tortoiseshell (Plate 37) were used, but marquetry was uncommon. While ebony and ebonised woods seem to have been regarded as too sombre and overpowering for long-case clocks, and were soon abandoned in favour of brighter decoration, the bracket clocks retained these dark woods, probably because their smaller size showed off the fire-gilt brass and silver mounts to greater effect. Between about 1675 and 1700 the low domes on the more expensive bracket clocks developed into taller, two-tiered 'double basket tops' (Plate 27) which were made of pierced metal, usually cast and chased brass; besides being of attractive appearance these were completely functional, for they enclosed the bell or bells. In plainer clocks, apertures in such forms as fretted friezes or side frets allowed the sound of striking to carry.

Some Technical Changes. STRIKING. In addition to striking the hours, clocks after 1660 struck the quarters, as Continental clocks had done since the 15th century. Bells of different tone distinguished the quarters from the hours. Sometimes the quarters chimed, and this was done by means of a chime barrel, usually with six or eight bells, worked by a third train. More rarely, the system of *grande sonnerie* was employed, by which the four quarters were struck on one or two bells, striking once, twice, three and four times, and the hour was repeated on a bell of different tone after each quarter (Plate 37). Most of these various methods of striking and chiming were applied to spring-driven clocks.

When the bracket clock was carried into the bedroom for the night, an ingenious device known as 'repeating work'—as it was called by William Derham in *The Artificial Clock-Maker*, 1696—enabled it to tell the time, when required, in the dark. A cord at the side of the clock was pulled to operate a mechanism which struck the last hour, or the last quarter followed by the last hour. This device, which avoided the necessity of using the tinder-box to strike a light, was invented by an Englishman, the Rev. Edward Barlow, in 1676. It was only very rarely found on long-case clocks as they were not intended for bedrooms. A 'strike/silent' dial enabled the clock owner, by moving a pointer, to put the strike out of action or restore it (See Figs 11, 12 and 13).

EQUATION OF TIME. Reference has already been made (p. 11) to the equation of time, the difference between solar time indicated on the sundial, and mean time shown on the clock. This difference, known from early times only to astronomers, now became common knowledge among clock owners, for the pendulum clock was so accurate that when it was set by the sundial it was essential to know by how much, on any given day, solar time differed from mean time. There was, of course, in those days no other means of checking the clock's accuracy than by comparing it with the sundial. Special equation tables were printed which gave the variation on each day of the year (Plate 80). The sundial would be read at a convenient time, say twelve noon on a sunny day, and, if the table showed that the clock should be six minutes faster, it was set at 12.06 p.m. Another method was to add an equation

37. Bracket clock by Tompion and Banger, the case decorated with tortoiseshell veneers and fire-gilt
mouldings and ornaments. *Grande sonnerie* striking on six bells. *c.* 1705.

38. Dial of clock by Tompion and Banger.

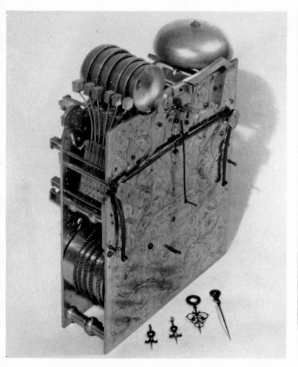 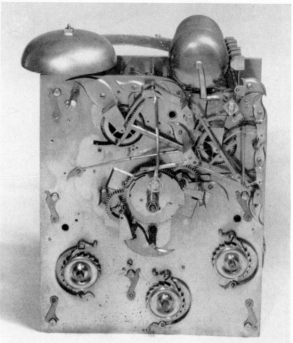

39. Back plate of clock by Tompion and Banger.　40. Front plate of clock by Tompion and Banger.

dial to the clock face (Fig. 14 and Plate 76). One such device took the form of two rims each marked with minutes on the chapter ring, the inner one fixed, the outer one (for solar time) moving. The minute hand thus read mean and solar time together. Equation dials were found on long-case clocks only; it was not considered worth while to use them on the less accurate spring-driven clocks.

MAINTAINING POWER. The driving force of both the weight- and spring-driven clock became in-effective while it was being wound up. Moreover, the teeth of the escape wheel were liable to damage through running backwards during winding. The problem was particularly serious for thirty-hour weight-driven clocks, for they could lose half a minute or more at each daily winding, which was done by pulling on one of the ropes or chains. Huygens overcame the problem for these clocks by inventing an 'endless rope' (or cord or chain) which enabled the weight to continue exerting power on the train while it was being wound up (Fig. 4). Most clocks that went for eight days or longer did not need this refinement, for the loss of time, spread over a longer interval (the eight-day clock was wound once a week, the month clock once a month, and so on) was not so serious.

It was, however, a different matter with the special clocks (known as 'regulator clocks') which were designed to be as accurate as possible, and for these a spring was used to press a lever against a tooth of one of the wheels to keep it going during winding. One device to carry this out was the 'bolt and shutter'. The keyhole of the going train—clocks going for eight days and longer were wound with a key inserted through a hole in the dial—was covered with a small metal shutter which, when moved aside to allow the key to be inserted, automatically set off the spring-loaded lever. Maintaining power was very rarely fitted to spring-driven clocks.

CALENDAR, LUNAR, TIDAL, ASTRONOMICAL AND ASTROLOGICAL DIALS. Besides giving accurate time, clocks were now harnessed to providing all kinds of information which in those days was of great importance.

Newspapers of a sort were beginning to appear, but not daily, and they reached only a tiny fraction of the population. Printed calendars were also rare. There was thus a real difficulty in keep-

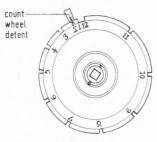

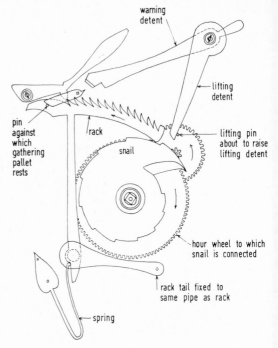

Fig. 11. The count wheel, more generally known as the locking plate, a metal disc with notched rim used on earlier clocks to determine the number of blows struck on the bell for hour striking. When the hammer strikes, the locking plate turns and the detent (or locking device) is raised and either falls on the rim, in which case the striking continues, or into a notch, when the striking stops. The notches are cut at increasing distances to allow striking from one to twelve. There is no rim space for one o'clock as the detent drops back into the same notch (Plate 20).

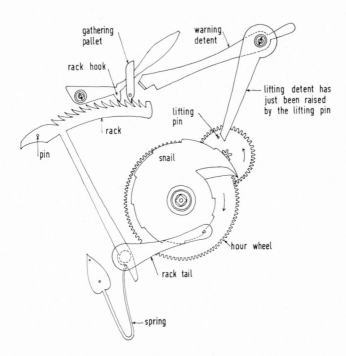

Fig. 12. (*Above*) Rack and snail striking—1. This method replaced the count wheel or locking plate (Fig. 11) after its invention by the Rev. Edward Barlow in 1676. The rack is a lever with ratchet teeth on the longer arm and a pin on the shorter. The snail (so called from its shape) is a disc which is attached to the hour wheel and is cut into a series of steps. It takes one hour for the snail to pass from one step to the next and twelve hours for it to make a complete turn. When the clock is about to strike the rack is released and falls to the left. The lower end drops on the snail and places the rack in such a position that the gathering pallet can gather a number of teeth corresponding to the depth of the step on the snail. When the clock strikes the rack is wound back and this counts the number of blows struck (Plate 40).

Fig. 13. Rack and snail striking—2. The clock ready to strike at the 10 o'clock position.

ing a check on the date, as people, even today, may find if they are away from home for long without a newspaper. Almost all long-case and bracket clocks after 1660 had a calendar aperture, usually rectangular or square, but sometimes round, through which the day of the month appeared on a ring that was mechanically operated once every twenty-four hours. A favourite position for the aperture was inside the chapter ring above the figure VI (Plates 15, 21 and 41). The calendar ring had thirty-one teeth and so had to be adjusted by hand back to 1 at the end of any month with less than

Fig. 14. Equation dial on a clock by Daniel Quare, *c.* 1695. The long hand, taking 365 days to turn, points to the day of the month. The hand with the figure of the sun shows by how many minutes a true sundial is faster or slower than the clock.

thirty-one days. Some clocks also displayed the name of the month. Exceptional examples had perpetual calendar work which did not require any hand adjustment as they registered the correct date by allowing for the varying length of the months and even for leap years.

It will be remembered that medieval mechanical clocks, like that at Wells, showed the age and phases of the moon. It still remained an urgent matter for people to know the state of the moon, for it was dangerous, in those days of very inadequate lighting, to venture out after dusk unless there was a full moon. Even in the late 18th century the famous Lunar Society of the Midlands, which included distinguished men like Josiah Wedgwood, James Watt, Matthew Boulton and Joseph Priestley, could meet in rotation in their homes only once a month at full moon—hence their name. Late Stuart clocks began to incorporate moon dials, usually at first a circle within the chapter ring with a 'man-in-the-moon' face showing the phases of the moon (Plate 27) and an adjacent aperture showing its age (i.e. the lunar cycle of $29\frac{1}{2}$ days). Later these dials were set in the arch of the clock. They were found much more frequently on 18th-century clocks.

The moon dial was the simplest form of astronomical dial. Other forms of celestial movement were also introduced. As there was a close connection in the 17th century between astronomy and astrology, for there was a widespread belief in the influence of the planets on persons and events, special dials showed the courses of the planets and the position of the sun and moon in the zodiac.

The state of the tide concerns very few people today (apart from seafarers) except perhaps briefly during a seaside holiday. But in those days, when overseas and coastal trade was expanding, when rivers were the main means of internal transport, and when even in remoter areas it might be necessary to know when a river could be safely forded, the times of the tides at London and other principal ports were obviously of great importance. Once the relation between lunar and tidal cycles had been established, tidal dials were added to some clocks to give the times of high tide at a selected port on any day of the year. The twice-daily tides were marked on the lunar dial of $29\frac{1}{2}$ days, which was set according to the time of high tide at new moon at the port concerned.

Exports of English Clocks. From the later part of the 17th century until the end of the Georgian period there was a flourishing export trade in English clocks to all parts of the world. Holland, Germany, Denmark and Norway (then a joint kingdom), Spain, Portugal, Italy and Turkey were particularly good markets, as also, for obvious reasons, were the British colonies, notably America and the West Indies. In 1700, to take a sample year from the official Customs records, all these countries imported English clocks; so too did Russia, Sweden, Poland, Flanders and France. Travellers abroad will often come across these clocks today in museums, houses and churches. In

Spain, for example, two long-case clocks by Ellicott and by Spencer and Parkis, are in the sacristy of Granada Cathedral, and two by George Clarke are built into the ends of the mahogany choir stalls of Cordova Cathedral. In addition to the clocks which were exported in the normal course of trade, there were many more which were bought in England by merchants, visitors, sea-captains and agents and taken back home as their personal possessions or as commissions for friends. In 1738, for instance, Thomas Hancock of Boston, Mass., ordered a clock from London through his agent there. Towards the end of the 18th century, Thomas Wagstaff, a Quaker clock-maker of London, provided lodgings for American Quakers who often took back his clocks with them.

Some London makers specialised in particular overseas markets, often incorporating the appropriate foreign names or numerals on the dials of their clocks (Plate 27). Markwick Markham of the Royal Exchange built up an extensive export trade with Turkey in the early part of the 18th century. Later, Higgs and Evans, also of the Royal Exchange, are said to have enjoyed practically a monopoly of the Spanish market. About the same time, James Cox, famous as the maker of expensive and ingenious musical clocks, developed exports to the Far East when British influence was growing in India. Some clock-makers in the Wapping and Stepney area of London, where there was an active colony of Norwegian timber importers, had special connections with Norway, selling their clocks to their Norwegian neighbours, or exporting direct to Norway. One of these makers, John Meredith, 'at the Dial and Ring near Ratcliffe Cross', had his trade card printed in both English and Norwegian. Norwegians had a special fondness for English clocks, and even remote farm-houses in Norway in the early 18th century had their English long-case or bracket clock (See also Plate 51).

Some Famous Makers. It will be possible here to mention only a very few of the pioneer clock-makers of the late Stuart period, the most formative epoch of English clock-making. All these distinguished makers worked in London, though a number learnt their craft in the provinces. The names of the Fromanteel family and of William Clement have already been mentioned in connection with, respectively, the first English-made pendulum clocks and the anchor escapement. A prominent early maker was Edward East (1602–97), clock-maker to both Charles I and Charles II. Among his products were night clocks, including the only known long-case night clock, which made provision for a light to shine through specially designed perforated dials. East lived for so long that until recently it was thought there must have been two men, father and son. Another early clock-making family was the Knibbs, of whom Joseph (1640-1711) became the most famous. He began his career at Oxford, where he worked for the University, but later migrated to London. He introduced into England 'Roman striking', which used a small bell for the I's and a large bell for the V's. The small bell strikes up to III; IV is one stroke on the small bell plus one stroke on the large bell; V is one stroke on the large bell, two strokes on the large bell represent the numeral X, and so on. This system conserved the power needed for the striking train, and clocks using it have IV and not IIII on their dials (Plate 18).

The greatest name of all is that of Thomas Tompion (1639–1713), sometimes called 'the father of English clock-making'. His fame was recognised in his own lifetime for William Derham (*op. cit.*) described him in 1696 as 'the famous artist'. Though Tompion can be credited with only one patent specification, his clocks are always stamped with a master's hand. As well as movements of great intricacy, incorporating equation work, perpetual calendar work and elaborate repeating work, he produced clockwork of simple design by division of labour among his craftsmen, each man specialising in making one part of the movement. The clock-cases showed the same trend towards simplicity, ebony and figured walnut being favoured choices (Plates 30–40).

Tompion worked from about 1674 in close collaboration with Robert Hooke, for whom he made instruments in addition to clocks and watches. Hooke invented a wheel-tooth cutting engine which undoubtedly increased the accuracy of Tompion's clockwork. Among Tompion's masterpieces are two clocks which he made for John Flamsteed, the first Astronomer Royal, at Greenwich Observatory, about 1675–6. They have survived (though not *in situ*) and have fourteen-foot, two-seconds pendulums and year movements—probably the first year movements made in England.

41. Dial of clock by Watson.

42. Long-case clock, the case decorated with floral marquetry.
By Samuel Watson, London, c. 1705.

Tompion made clocks for King William III, whose cypher they bear. One of these, a long-case clock in walnut of beautiful figure, made about 1695–1700, has a three-month movement and perpetual calendar work with allowance for leap years; another, made about 1700, is a remarkable spring-driven bracket clock in a veneered ebony case with silver mounts, which goes for a year and strikes the hours and quarters, the large barrels and fusees for the going and striking being housed in a large box-like base with a glazed aperture for observing the pendulum.

Tompion was one of the first makers to number his clocks (about 550 have been traced to him) and to use the broken arch dial. A well-known early example of the latter is the long-case one-month clock presented in 1709 by Tompion to the Pump Room, Bath, where it still stands. The arched top in this instance accommodates an equation of time register.

Two clock-makers associated with Tompion are Edward Banger (Plate 37) and George Graham (c. 1673–1751), both his nephews by marriage and both his partners. The Tompion-Banger partnership lasted from about 1701 to 1708 and was productive of many fine clocks. Graham, who succeeded to Tompion's business, and was later elected a Fellow of the Royal Society, invented the dead beat escapement about 1715 and the mercury pendulum in the 1720s (see p. 61), both of which are still in use today. He was buried in the same grave as Tompion in Westminster Abbey, though this was not then the special honour that it would be now.

One of Tompion's great rivals was Daniel Quare (1647–1724). Although as a Quaker he could not take the oath of allegiance and thus be officially appointed a royal clock-maker, he nevertheless made clocks for the Crown. He is particularly associated with the earliest equation clocks and long-case clocks with one-year movements. A very fine example of the latter, made about 1705, is still in the King's State Bedroom at Hampton Court Palace. After two-and-a-half centuries its veneered walnut case has acquired a most attractive golden colour.

4. The Georgian Period, 1714-1830

General Features. Much of the fine craftsmanship, good design and inventive genius which distinguished late Stuart clock-making continued in the succeeding Georgian period. Some Georgian clock cases were masterpieces of the furniture-maker's craft, as befitted the 'golden age' of English cabinet-making, when outstanding figures like Chippendale, Adam and Sheraton included clock cases among their furniture designs. There were also notable advances in the accuracy of clock movements. On the other hand, the great economic and social changes of the Industrial Revolution profoundly affected the structure of the clock-making industry. The late Stuart industry had been dominated by craftsmen-shopkeepers who made and sold their clocks to a relatively small group of well-to-do clients. Now the market widened considerably with the rising standard of living, and the numbers of provincial makers increased rapidly after 1750.

As the output of clocks rose, through more minute sub-division of labour and the increased use of machines for cutting geared wheels, fusees, etc—methods which were already known in the 17th century but were now extended—there was a gradual decline in general quality and design. A division arose between making and selling. A common feature of London and other large towns was the retailing shopkeeper who sold clocks and watches which were no longer made on his premises, but were supplied to him by middlemen who supervised the outworkers, each specialising in the production of only one part of the clockwork. Clerkenwell became the centre in London for workers of this kind. Thus Georgian clock-making had two aspects, the continuation of the highest standards by gifted craftsmen, and the increasing production of cheaper clocks of mediocre quality.

'We beat all Europe in Clocks and Watches of all sorts', writes R. Campbell in *The London Tradesman*, 1747, 'and export those useful Engines to all Parts of the Known World'. But he adds in his description of the sub-division of labour that the watch- and clock-maker 'puts his Name upon the Plate, and is esteemed the Maker, though he has not made in his Shop the smallest Wheel belonging to it'.

Stylistic Changes and Decoration. During the reigns of the first two Georges (1714–60) marquetry decoration of long-case clocks went out of fashion, more favoured methods being finely figured walnut veneers (Plates 45 and 48), and japanning. For japanned cases, common ground colours were green, red, blue and black, and, more rarely, yellow, white and scarlet. The ornament was applied to this ground in gold or polychrome. Sometimes the pattern was an imitation of tortoiseshell. Japanning was only occasionally used on bracket clocks for which ebony remained strongly in favour until supplanted by mahogany after 1750.

Mahogany was beginning to challenge the supremacy of walnut during the second quarter of the century. In 1721, Parliament, in order to increase the supplies of timber for the navy, passed an act to free British colonial timbers from their heavy import duties and thus make them cheaper. The act stimulated trade generally in colonial timbers and there was an increase in the imports of fine furniture woods, of which the West Indies were a fertile source of supply and mahogany their choicest product. It was some time, however, before the beautifully figured, light-coloured walnut veneers on long-case clocks were superseded, for the earliest shipments of mahogany were of dark-toned and close-grained 'Spanish' wood which, as the example of ebony had shown, was regarded as being too overpowering for tall cases. Not until after 1750, when mahogany of attractive figure was available, did walnut finally go out of fashion.

From about 1740 to 1760 long-case clocks were temporarily eclipsed in favour by hanging and bracket clocks. These smaller varieties were more suitable for displaying the asymmetrical C and S scrolls of the rococo style which Chippendale popularised in his *Gentleman and Cabinet-Maker's Director* (1754) (Plates 52, 54 and 55). This pattern-book included a number of designs for both bracket and long-case clocks, but few appear to have been executed. Some long-case clocks of this

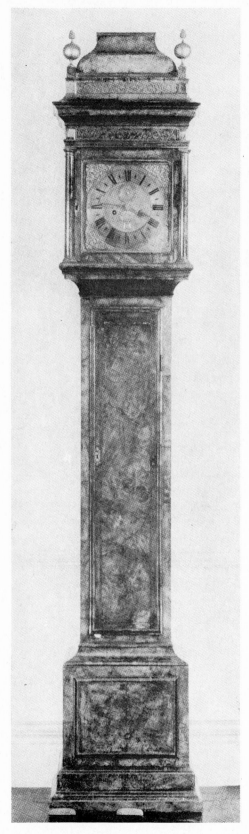

43. Long-case clock, the case veneered with walnut. By Daniel Delander, London, *c*. 1715.

44. Dial of clock by Delander.

45. (*Opposite*) Long-case clock, the case veneered with burr walnut. *c*. 1725.

46. (*Opposite*) Long-case clock, the case veneered with burr ash. Unusual combination of pediment and arched dial. *c*. 1715.

47. 'Act of Parliament' clock, the case painted black. By Humphrey Sellon, Southwark. Mid 18th century.

48. Long-case clock, the case veneered with walnut and decorated with carved masks and leaf ornament. Mid 18th century.

49. Bracket clock in red lacquer case by John Jullion, Brentford. *c* 1730.

50. Back plate of clock by Jullion.

time are loosely described as 'Chippendale clocks' as they have scrolled or fretted pediments which recall, usually faintly, some of the mannerisms of the *Director*. A number of bracket clocks, however, were decidedly rococo in character, their decoration being crisply carved in mahogany. Other bracket clocks had pagoda tops, fretwork and similar Chinese motifs which Chippendale also presented in the *Director* (Plate 56).

After 1760, until about 1790, Robert Adam's neo-classical style became fashionable, and the

51. Mid 18th-century Norwegian bracket clock showing English influence, the case decorated with red japan. The japanner, N. Löchstör, learnt his craft in London.

52. Cartel timepiece in carved and gilded wood case. Movement by James Scholefield, London. *c.* 1750–5.

long-case clock returned to favour. It was now often veneered with figured mahogany or with other choice woods (Plate 63). Inlay and painting were also employed. Crossbandings of satinwood were particularly popular. In the last quarter of the 18th century London makers produced some fine long-case clocks of mahogany inlaid with simple designs such as shells or flowers in the centre and corners of the trunk and base, and in the top of the hood. A special kind of case of this time was the 'horn-top', so named from its scrolled ogee pediment.

By about 1800 the long-case clock was at last becoming obsolete in London. Sheraton, who included designs for these cases in his *Drawing Book* of 1791–4, writes in his *Cabinet Dictionary* of 1803 that 'as these pieces are almost obsolete in London, I have given no designs for any; but intend to do it in my large work [his unfinished *Encyclopaedia* of 1805] to serve my country friends'.

Special Types of Georgian Clock. REGULATORS. Special attention was paid in the Georgian period and later to regulators, the name given to clocks of extreme accuracy (Plates 57 and 79). Strictly speaking, they should be called timepieces, as they usually excluded striking, calendar, lunar and

Fig. 15. Graham's mercury pendulum. Adjustment of the quantity of mercury in the container keeps the centre of oscillation of the pendulum constant. In warm weather, for instance, the mercury expands upwards to compensate for the downward expansion of the pendulum rod.

Fig. 16. Conventional representation of the gridiron pendulum, with iron (or steel) and brass rods. As the rate of expansion of brass to iron is in the ratio of about 3:2, the downward expansion of the iron rods is balanced by the upward expansion of the brass rods when heated, and thus the centre of oscillation of the pendulum remains constant.

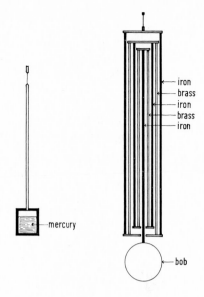

similar work. They were weight-driven and had maintaining power. They were soon found in observatories, clock-makers' workshops, clock and watch retailers and large households. Their use increased after about 1760 as the pace of industrialisation quickened in England and they continued to be made well after domestic long-case clocks had gone out of fashion. Users of improved means of transport and communications—mail-coaches, carriers, shipping lines and railways—all found regulators essential for keeping to their time-tables. So also, as life became geared to the clock, did the growing number of factories, offices, business concerns and scientific institutions.

Early in the Georgian period regulators incorporated a number of technical improvements of which the dead-beat escapement and the compensated pendulum were the most notable. A defect of the anchor escapement, accurate though it was for ordinary domestic clocks, was its recoil, which can be easily detected by watching the seconds hand of a long-case clock. This recoil was eliminated by George Graham's invention about 1715 of the dead-beat escapement, a modified form of the anchor escapement which stopped the second hand dead between each beat. For over two centuries this escapement has been used for regulators.

A compensated pendulum is one that maintains a constant length during changes of temperature, compensating, that is, for the expansion and contraction of the metal pendulum in warm and cold weather which make it swing slower or faster. Graham, after experimenting with a variety of metals, found that mercury had a much higher rate of expansion than solids. In the 1720s he devised a pendulum with a bob in the form of a jar of mercury. The level of the mercury rose or fell with the rise and fall in temperature, countering the changes in the length of the pendulum rod (in hot weather, for example, the upward expansion of the mercury compensated for the downward expansion of the rod) and keeping its centre of oscillation constant (Fig. 15 and Plate 57). At about the same time the 'gridiron' pendulum was introduced. This took its name from its alternate rods of steel and brass, and worked on the principle that the rate of expansion of brass is about 50 per cent greater than that of steel (Fig. 16 and Plate 78). The invention of the gridiron pendulum has been attributed to John Harrison, the famous chronometer-maker (see p. 68), or to him and his brother James conjointly, but evidence now appears to favour James as the inventor. James also seems to have invented the 'grasshopper' escapement which until recently has always been credited to John. This escapement was delicate, noiseless and almost frictionless, and did not require oiling. It never came into general use, however, though it was later occasionally employed by the well-known Vulliamy clock-making family.

53. Marbled pedestal to contain weights and pendulum of the clock by Pyke (Plate 54).

54. (*Opposite*) Mahogany clock by John Pyke, clock-maker to the Prince of Wales, the case decorated with fine rococo carving in the style of William Vile. *c*. 1760.

55. Musical table clock in case of carved mahogany, based on a design in Chippendale's *Director* (3rd ed., 1762). Movement by Alexander Cumming. *c*. 1765.   56. Bracket clock in pagoda-topped case of mahogany carved and decorated with fret-cutting. Movement by Thomas Wynn, London. *c*. 1765–70.

CARTEL CLOCKS. In the decade before 1750 wall clocks of French origin, known as cartel clocks, became fashionable (Plate 52). Made of carved and gilded soft wood, or of gilded bronze, with a scrolled and sometimes pierced frame in the rococo taste, they looked highly decorative against the rich wall hangings of the period. To solve the problem of taking these (and other hanging and bracket) clocks down from the wall and opening the back door every time they had to be started or stopped, a small disc called a 'false bob' was suspended from the front of the pallet arbor of the verge escapement. This showed through an aperture in the dial and thus the clocks could be dealt with from the front (Plate 38).

MUSICAL CLOCKS. Musical clocks which became popular in the 18th century (Plate 55) usually played a tune every hour, the music being provided by a pin barrel (similar to that in a musical box) which operated bell hammers. The more bells a clock had, the greater was its range of tunes. If several tunes were available, a lever in the tune indicator (often situated in the arch above the dial) could be pointed to the selected tune; this shifted the barrel axially and put a different set of pins into operation. Musical clocks which also chimed had four trains, for going, striking, chiming and music. In some cases the chime was omitted and the clock played a tune every three or four hours. Most musical clocks had a music/silent dial which could be worked to stop the music performance, just as the strike/silent dial could stop the striking. Other types—organ clocks—used pipes and bellows instead of bells and hammers, and some very ·ingenious varieties were made. Numerous 'mechanical curiosities' of this nature, incorporating clocks and different musical instruments, were

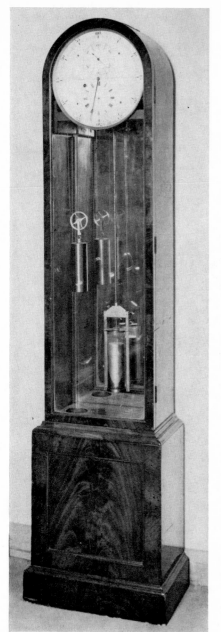

57. Regulator timepiece with mercury pendulum in mahogany case by F. Pearce, Newington Causeway. Second half of 18th century.

58. Cabinet of mahogany cross-banded with satinwood, with clock inscribed 'Weeks's Museum'. As well as being fully equipped as a bookcase and dressing table, this cabinet incorporated an automatic organ in the cupboard worked by the clock mechanism. *c.* 1790–1800.

59. Balloon bracket clock in case of ebonised pearwood. Movement by Julian Leroux, Charing Cross.
End of 18th century.

60. Bracket clock in stepped-top case veneered with ebony and inlaid with brass. Movement by
Brockbank and Atkins, c. 1800.

exhibited in the late Georgian period at Weeks's Museum, a famous London show-place near Piccadilly (Plate 58).

ACT OF PARLIAMENT CLOCKS. A type of hanging, weight-driven clock with a large unglazed dial and a small trunk has been wrongly called an 'Act of Parliament clock'. This type is supposed to have been introduced by inn-keepers for the benefit of their customers when many people gave up their clocks and watches after William Pitt had imposed a tax on them in 1797. The effect on the industry was so disastrous that the act was repealed in 1798. Very few such clocks, therefore, could have been made between 1797–8, and in fact their design was already familiar well before 1750 (Plates 47 and 64).

61. Interior of watch-maker's shop from *The Book of English Trades* (1827 ed.), showing types of clocks then in use and craftsman's lathe worked by a bow.

BALLOON CLOCKS. The balloon type of bracket clock that was popular after 1775 until the end of the Regency period (1830) had, as its name implies, a circular dial and a 'waist' of graceful curves (Plate 59). Specimens of good quality were made of ebonised pearwood and ormolu mounts, or of figured mahogany with bandings of tulipwood, rosewood and kingwood and inlaid decoration. After 1800 bracket clocks by the best makers were made in many of the prevalent Regency woods— mahogany, rosewood, ebony and satinwood—with brass 'stringing' (i.e. thin inlaid lines) in the darker woods and ebonised stringing in the lighter (Plate 60).

THE MARINE CHRONOMETER. In the second half of the 18th century English horologists took the lead in the development of the marine chronometer. The problem of accurate time-keeping at sea, essential for determining a ship's longitude when out of sight of land, became ever more urgent as long ocean trade routes were opened. Clock-makers had wrestled with the problem throughout the 17th century without a satisfactory result. In 1714 the British government offered a reward of £10,000 for the invention of a timekeeper that could determine a ship's longitude to within an accuracy of 1° for a voyage to the West Indies, and £15,000 and £20,000 if the accuracy were within 40′ and 30′ respectively. After designing and making three timekeepers, John Harrison (1693–1776), a carpenter's son from Yorkshire, eventually won the last-named sum with a chronometer made in

62. Casket clock, the case decorated with ormolu and Bilston plaques. The hinged upper part discloses a velvet-lined casket. Late 18th century.

63. Mahogany long-case clock by Mitchell and Mott, New York, showing English neo-classical influence. Late 18th century.

64. 'Act of Parliament' clock by Thomas Mudge in japanned case. Late 18th century.

65. Two mahogany North Country long-case clocks by (*left*) Barker of Wigan, *c.* 1780, and (*right*) Shepley of Manchester, late 18th century.

66. Clock of Derby biscuit porcelain decorated with ormolu. Movement by Benjamin Vulliamy, London, showing French influence. *c.* 1800.

67. Long-case clock, the case decorated with japan. Late 18th century.   68. Long-case clock in case of finely figured mahogany, with fretted crest and finials. Late 18th century.

69. French mantel clock by Lepaute, decorated with ormolu, of the type which influenced English clock-makers. *c.* 1800.

1759 and now known as 'Harrison's No 4'. Though this was essentially a large watch, it embodied Harrison's previous experiments with spring-driven clocks and was marvellously accurate, being only 5 seconds out (equivalent to an error of about $1\frac{1}{2}$ miles) on a voyage to Jamaica in 1761. It was adapted to changes in temperature and had a remontoire, a device for frequent rewinding of the spring (in this case every $7\frac{1}{2}$ seconds) to keep its pull constant. The extraordinary skill and beauty of Harrison's work was admired by the artist, William Hogarth, who writes in his *Analysis of Beauty* (1753) that Mr Harrison's clock 'for keeping time at sea . . . perhaps is one of the most exquisite movements ever made'.

Thomas Mudge (1715–94) (Plate 64), who was a former apprentice of George Graham, and is generally credited with the invention of the detached lever escapement (used mainly in watches, but also in travelling clocks), followed Harrison in designing marine chronometers and won an award given by the Board of Longitude. But both Harrison's and Mudge's mechanisms were too complicated and expensive for general use at sea. The credit for making chronometers that were accurate and simple enough for commercial production goes to John Arnold (1736–99) and Thomas Earnshaw (1774–1829), working independently. England's lead in the manufacture of chronometers, to which increasing numbers of clock- and watch-makers now turned their attention, was maintained throughout the 19th century and was of particular value to British shipping in the French wars of 1793–1815 (Plate 87).

70. Clock by Vulliamy, on
satinwood stand with painted
panel by Cipriani. *c.* 1780.

71. Bracket clock (on original bracket) in case of figured mahogany, with elaborate ormolu mounts, silvered dial and 'inverted bell' top. Movement by Salmon, London. *c*. 1775.

72. Small bracket clock by George Tupman, London. End of 18th century.

73. Movement of clock by Tupman.

Later Georgian Developments. Just as dials had reflected the technical improvements in timekeeping, so they now reflected the changes resulting from increased production of cheaper clocks. In early long-case clocks the dials were almost always of brass with a separate silvered brass chapter ring and decorative cast metal spandrels. Dials of good quality clocks had their centre circles matted, i.e. given a rough finish by punching, a laborious process which was later speeded up by the use of a spiked steel roller. Other finishes, such as clear, silvered or engraved brass, were also found. About 1775 the iron dial came into use on long-case clocks. There was no separate chapter ring, for the ring and numerals were painted in black on a white ground, and it was customary to add decorative scenes. These painted dials are sometimes considered as typical examples of degeneration, especially as spandrels disappeared when they came into fashion, but it would be wrong to dismiss them all in this way, for many were still well designed and were fitted into excellent cases. Modern dealers have been known to replace the painted dial by a brass one to enhance the clock's value.

After 1750 some bracket clocks and especially watches were fitted with enamel dials which greatly improved their legibility (Plate 72). Long-case clocks, however, whose larger dials were in any case easier to read, very rarely had enamel dials as they were difficult and expensive to make in a large size.

Clock-making flourished in many provincial towns after 1750, particularly in northern England where the trade was encouraged by the rising industrial prosperity (Plate 65). The typical North

74. Long-case clock in mahogany by John Holmes, London, c. 1790.
75. Long-case equation clock by William Dutton, London, in mahogany case. c. 1775.

76. Dial and equation dial of clock by Dutton.

77. Movement of clock by
Dutton.

Country long-case clock differed from its London counterpart in its standardised movement, greater
width, higher base and shorter trunk, and in the use of fretwork and carving on its case of mahogany
or of oak veneered or crossbanded with mahogany. Provincial makers—Sheraton's 'country friends'
—continued to turn out long-case clocks, which grew broader as the years progressed, after London
makers had begun to concentrate on portable clocks, but by about 1820 the long-case clock as a
general product was almost extinct, lingering on through the 19th century in the hands of a few
specialists.

Important provincial centres produced a number of makers of excellent skill and standards. But
the standardisation which developed from the outworker system meant that retailing clock-makers,
as Campbell pointed out, could buy not merely separate parts of their clocks from suppliers but
whole movements as well, on which their names might be engraved and which they had fitted into
cases made by their local case-makers. That is why today numbers of clocks have identical movements
and cases but different clock-makers' names.

The transition from hand craft to machine production was a very slow one, and if eventually

F

78. Gridiron pendulum of clock by Dutton.

79. Regulator timepiece by Vulliamy in mahogany case. 1783.

80. Equation table
found, with
directions for setting
up, inside the
Vulliamy regulator.

clocks lost their attractive hand-made features, some were a long time disappearing. Clock hands, for instance, kept their evidence of the craftsman's skill almost to the very end, for it seems that their cutting out and filing was often the first job that an apprentice was set to when learning his trade. Blued steel (given its colour by heated sand) and brass were the materials, brass hands on later clocks being cast and finished by hand. Brass hands were particularly fashionable when silvered dials with engraved centres were revived on North Country clocks in the late 18th century.

Prevailing trends are exemplified in the history of two famous clock-making families of the period, Vulliamy and Ellicott. Three generations of the Vulliamy family—Justin (1712–97), the Swiss founder of the firm, Benjamin (1747–1811), and Benjamin Louis, F.R.S. (1780–1854)—were clockmakers for over a century to five monarchs (Plates 66, 70 and 79). They occasionally used Harrison's grasshopper escapement and carried the highest standard of hand skill of the old order well into Victoria's reign. The firm of Ellicott was founded early in the 18th century, and the founder's son, John, F.R.S. (1706–72), was one of the most eminent makers of his day. At the end of the century, however, the family had become mainly a retailing business, and is known to have put its name on the dials of clocks for which the movements were supplied by outside sources.

5. Victorian and After

Imported Clocks. After 1830, when railways still further quickened the pace of industry, Britain became the first country in the world to achieve full industrialisation and to have a working population whose lives were strictly regulated by the clock. The need for cheap clocks and watches was therefore universal. When free trade was being established in the 1840s, this need was largely met by a flood of imports, mainly from France, Switzerland and America, where the factory system of watch and clock-making developed earlier than in England. Already in 1842 Adam Thomson (in his *Time and Timekeepers*) notes that England was the largest market for cheap foreign clocks 'probably from the larger portion of our labouring population requiring a knowledge of time', and he argues, with true Victorian earnestness, that everybody should own a good timekeeper to promote punctuality, for 'indifference to time invariably shows weakness or indolence of character, and is subversive of order and regularity'. The moral virtues of punctuality might be extolled, but the effect of free trade on the English clock- and watch-making industry was disastrous. In 1849, B. L. Vulliamy writes of the resulting large-scale unemployment among English operatives, though he also admits that he himself often sent watch cases to Geneva to be fitted with cheaper Swiss movements. When Gladstone further modified import duties in 1853, the official returns show that 135,000 clocks were imported in the last seven months of that year, and 228,000 in 1854, when 'it would seem that English mantelpieces were filling up rather rapidly with French clocks'. (Sir John Clapham, *Economic History of Modern Britain*, 1952, ii, 16). The growing competition from American clocks is emphasised repeatedly in the standard Victorian work, the *Rudimentary Treatise on Clock and Watch Making* (first published in 1850), by E. B. Denison, a distinguished amateur horologist who designed Big Ben and later became Lord Grimthorpe. Even English spring clocks, states Denison, which had previously held their own, 'are getting fast superseded by the better class of American clocks and by French ornamental clocks, neither of which, however, will last so long'.

The Great Exhibition, 1851. Clock-makers from France, Switzerland and Britain shared almost equally most of the large number of medals and honourable mentions which were awarded at the Great Exhibition of 1851 in London, where horology was a section of Class X of exhibits, devoted to 'Philosophical Instruments and their Dependent Processes'. Significantly, many awards were for methods which cut down costs of production, including two Council Medals, the highest awards of all, to E. J. Dent (whose firm made Big Ben) for a turret clock of great accuracy 'accomplished by a cheaper mode of construction', and to the Japy brothers of France for 'clock and watch movements made by machinery, much cheaper than any other movement and equally good'.

There were also, of course, many hand-made movements at the Exhibition which proved that the old skill continued. But too often the dials and cases of all types of clocks exemplified the eye-catching elaboration and straining after novelty which the Exhibition unfortunately encouraged. Not only was there a revival of many so-called 'historic' styles—Egyptian, Gothic, Elizabethan, Jacobean, Louis Quatorze, Louis Quinze, etc—but legibility was often sacrificed to ornament, as in the ornate enamel dial and hands of Moore and Son's 'skeleton' clock (a popular type which had its movement exposed under a glass dome), and in France's clock-face inscribed with numerous texts from Scripture. Though this lavish decoration was not typical (no more than it was in the furniture exhibits) of the best Victorian work, it certainly set trends of fashion for mass-produced debased versions, as could be seen in many clocks of the period, which were made in a very wide variety of materials.

Victorian Decoration. Almost without exception the numerous pattern books of furniture published in the early Victorian period totally ignore clock cases. It was customary, however, to have a large clock, usually accompanied by a barometer, in the hall of a mansion, and eight designs for hall clocks,

81. Four wall (bracket) clocks from Blackie's *Cabinet-Maker's Assistant* (1853) in Victorian versions of (Figs. 1 and 2) the Elizabethan, (Fig. 3) the Louis Quinze, and (Fig. 4) the Louis Quatorze styles.

82. Four long-case clocks from Blackie's *Cabinet-Maker's Assistant* (1853) in (Figs. 1 and 4) the Elizabethan, (Fig. 2) the Louis Quatorze, and (Fig. 3) the Louis Quinze styles.

83. Carriage clock, French movement in English case, with *grande sonnerie* striking, phases of the moon and perpetual calendar. Late 19th century.   84. Clock in shaped mahogany case with applied repoussé silver decoration in Art Nouveau style. French movement, Birmingham hall-mark. 1910.

four bracket and four long-case, are shown in Blackie's *Cabinet-Maker's Assistant* (1853), a vast repository of Victorian designs with full working instructions (Plates 81 and 82). These bracket clocks bear no relation to the old table variety; though supported on a bracket, or hanging from the wall, they now have a long trunk and resemble long-case clocks without their base. They conform to the 'three-quarter length' clocks which Denison strongly advocates in his book, and which he considers as cheap and as efficient as long-cases 'and very superior in appearance'. Such clocks, according to Blackie's *Assistant*, are 'usually made of oak, frequently of mahogany and sometimes of satinwood, or deal painted in flat tints, and the carving hatched with gilding'. Both types of clock in the book are designed in the popular versions of Elizabethan, Louis Quatorze and Louis Quinze styles, all of which required a great deal of applied ornament. Glazed doors in the trunk are advocated, but in some examples decoration of strapwork (for Elizabethan) and acanthus leaves (for Louis Quatorze) is also applied as fretwork behind the glass, and backed with a thin panel covered with coloured silk.

Two decorative materials which were fashionable in the mid-Victorian period, buhl and papier-mâché, were revivals from an earlier period. After 1815 the partiality for French furniture had encouraged many English imitations of buhl, the form of marquetry in brass and tortoiseshell (and other materials) which had been perfected by André-Charles Boulle (1642–1732). Clock cases now

85. English carriage clock. *c*. 1850.

86. Bracket clock in case of ebonised wood, with full repeat, enamel dial and chased gilt metal background.
c. 1850.

87. Marine chronometer. 19th century.

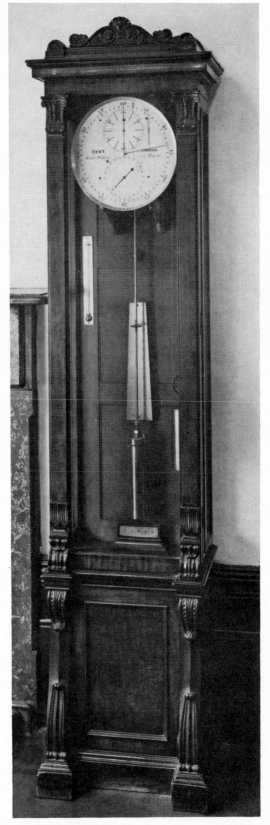

88. Regulator timepiece by Dent with escapement by
G. B. Airy, the Astronomer Royal. Late 19th century.

decorated in this manner often followed 18th-century designs so closely that it is difficult to distinguish between the two periods. Ornamental brackets in papier-mâché for clocks were being designed by 1840 by C. F. Bielefeld, the chief London maker of the material. No long-case clocks seem to have been made of papier-mâché, but it was used for other types of clock, including the Act of Parliament variety.

In the last quarter of the century concern with the deterioration in general standards of design and craftsmanship increasingly turned the attention of leading designers and architects to a serious study of furniture. The Arts and Crafts movement of the 1880s and later, inspired by William Morris, saw the creation of guilds of craftsmen, designers and architects who combined aims of social reform with skilled and honest workmanship in articles of good design which they demonstrated through numerous exhibitions. Many Georgian techniques were revived, such as marquetry and inlay, sometimes incorporating metalwork, enamel, mother-of-pearl and other materials. As a result, some interesting designs for hand-made clock cases fitted with machine-made movements were produced, but too often (as happened to furniture generally) they were taken up by the trade and copied indiscriminately.

At the end of Victoria's reign the style known as Art Nouveau deliberately sought a new art form for the 20th century by turning its back on historical revivals and emphasising ornament based on natural forms, particularly that of vegetation, expressed in sinuous curves covering all available surfaces. Rapid commercialisation turned this into the 'Quaint Style' which was soon derided, but prominent Art Nouveau figures like M. H. Baillie Scott, C. R. Mackintosh and C. F. A. Voysey all designed clock cases. Art Nouveau absorbed the technical skills of the Arts and Crafts movement and affected almost every kind of material. Many homes still have mantel clocks in this style made of repoussé metal or of wood stained various colours or inlaid with tiles, metal, ivory and other woods (Plate 84). Often the clocks are inscribed with a motto or saying—a peculiar feature of the style.

Special Types of Victorian Clock. As already noted, Victoria's reign saw practically the end of the domestic long-case clock, which even the best horologists of the time seem to have regarded with indifference if not with antipathy. Denison, for instance, describes how he converted an old long-case clock into one of three-quarter length by cutting off its 'large and ugly and useless pedestal'—an operation which he obviously considered a great improvement. This strange act of vandalism was paralleled by B. L. Vulliamy who replaced movements by famous makers (including Tompion) with his own and added his name to the dial. Horologists then paid scant respect to antiques, and their attitude was exactly that of the contemporary architect, Sir Gilbert Scott, in his 'restoration' of Gothic churches. Regulators, however, were one medium which preserved both the form of the long-case clock and its traditional high standards of hand craft and design throughout the 19th century and continue to do so. They were essential for clock-makers to adjust their clocks to the correct time. Made mainly by hand, the precision of their movements was matched by the careful construction of their cases which were usually quite plain and thus in complete contrast to the ostentatious decoration of many domestic clocks (Plate 88).

Regulators themselves were still being checked by the sundial until about 1850. After that date, following Alexander Bain's pioneer application of electricity to horology in 1840, various systems of distant control from a master clock could be transmitted by electric current to towns, railway stations, etc, to synchronise regulators, until the broadcast of the Greenwich time signal by radio in the 1920s performed this function. Regulators then became much less common, though some are still made.

A special type of long-case clock was the 'tell-tale' or watchman's clock, the forerunner of the modern clocking-in machine. It was first produced by John Whitehurst, F.R.S. of Derby about 1750 and was made by his family firm into the Victorian period. Apart from their obvious use in factories, mills, etc, such clocks were also found in large households. They usually had narrow oak cases and a rotating dial with a series of metal pins set at half-hour positions. The watchman on his rounds

89. Rolling ball clock. A modern version of an old method of time-keeping which was known in the 16th century and reintroduced into England in 1808 by Sir William Congreve, Comptroller of Woolwich Laboratory.

depressed a pin which thus recorded the time of his visit.

The rapid improvements in travel during Victoria's reign led to a great vogue in the second half of the century, and particularly in the last quarter, for carriage clocks, the English term for the French *pendules de voyage*. Though nearly all these clocks came from France, where they were made in factories in large numbers, Vulliamy, Dent and others had made similar ones in England from the 1830s. Carriage clocks varied considerably in their movements, materials and design, but a common type had a brass base, four vertical pillars, front, side, back and top panels of glass (sides of brass, enamel, porcelain and other materials are also found), a hinged handle for portability, and a platform escapement (i.e. mounted on a separate plate to facilitate mass production and also repairs) (Plates 83 and 85). For travelling, the clock was fitted into a leather-covered box with an opening for the dial, which was often of white porcelain.

In specialist fields British clock designers continued to make important contributions to the advance of horological science. Many fine turret clocks were made for the new and imposing town halls which reflected the civic pride and dignity of great industrial cities. Sir George Airy, the Astronomer Royal from 1835 to 1881, designed a clock made by Dent for the Greenwich Observatory which kept 'Greenwich Mean Time' from 1870 to 1920 and represented the peak of mechanical accuracy in timekeeping before the advent of complete electrical control. Airy's clock was superseded by W. H. Shortt's free pendulum clock which was perfected in 1921–4 and is the most accurate pendulum clock ever made, its pendulum swinging in complete freedom, with no work to do at all, as it receives an impulse every half minute from an electric 'slave' clock. This Shortt clock marks the

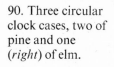

90. Three circular clock cases, two of pine and one (*right*) of elm.

final chapter in the story which began in 1657 when Huygens first successfully applied the pendulum to clockwork. It is amazingly accurate, its daily variation being only a few thousandths of a second. It is still in use in small observatories but is now replaced in large ones by the even more accurate quartz crystal and atomic clocks. It must be pointed out, however, that many horologists do not consider electric domestic clocks to be true clocks, regarding them as meters recording the consumption of current in units of time, quite different from mechanical devices motivated by weights or springs.

Antiquarian horology, fostered by the general revival of interest in craftsmanship and good design, and by the work of such bodies as the British Horological Institute (founded 1858) and the Antiquarian Horological Society (founded 1953), is today a well-established study which has done much to preserve old clocks, to unearth information about their makers and to arouse appreciation of their fine traditions. We now condemn both the Victorians' disrespect for antique clocks and the poor design of so many of their own.

We must also, however, accept the conditions of our own day. Only the machine methods of modern industry can produce clocks quickly and cheaply enough to satisfy the needs of a population vastly greater than that of the age when hand production was the sole method. Very rarely today do we find examples of clocks made entirely by hand (Plate 89). Moreover, ours is a utilitarian attitude to clocks. Their cases are no longer made to attract our attention; they are there to tell us the time only when we need to know it. Their decoration is thus subordinate to their function, the dial is more important than the case, and simplicity is their keynote. All these points are worth the serious consideration of industrial designers, for the problems of achieving high standards of appearance and legibility can be resolved in a variety of ways and with an ever-increasing variety of materials. The traditions of fine craftsmanship have far more to offer than mere nostalgia for the past. They have bequeathed us accuracy in time-keeping, which we can insist on in all our clocks, and they can equally well ensure the best quality of design in the cases.

91. (*Above*) Three clock cases, each a solid block of elm, and (*below*) three clock cases of yew.

Select Bibliography

Baillie, G. H. *Watchmakers and Clockmakers of the World*. 2nd ed., 1947.

Baillie, G. H. *Clocks and Watches: an Historical Bibliography*. 1951

Britten, F. J. *Old Clocks and Watches and their Makers*. 7th. ed., 1956.

Britten, F. J. *The Watch and Clock Maker's Handbook, Dictionary and Guide*. 15th. ed., 1955.

de Carle, D. *Watch and Clock Encyclopedia*. 2nd. ed., 1959.

Denison, E. B. (Baron Grimthorpe). *Clocks, Watches and Bells*. 7th. ed., 1883.

Edwardes, E. L. *The Grandfather Clock*. 1952

Lloyd, H. Alan. *The Collector's Dictionary of Clocks*. 1964.

Lloyd, H. Alan. *Some Outstanding Clocks over 700 Years, 1250–1950*. 1958.

Lloyd, H. Alan. *Chats on Old Clocks*. 1959.

Lloyd, H. Alan. *The English Domestic Clock*. 1938.

Symonds, R. W. *A Book of English Clocks*. Revised ed., 1950.

Symonds, R. W. *Thomas Tompion, his Life and Work*. 1951.

Ward, F. A. B. *Time Measurement*. Part I: Historical Review. 1961.

Index